Ohhhh, I Can Be That with Esa!

Esa~Bella that is.

Story by
Audrey C. Johnson McCurdy

Illustrated by
Henry Bosak

Ohhhh, I Can Be That with Esa! Esa~Bella that is!

Story By
Audrey C. JohnsonMcCurdy

Illustrated By
Henry Bosak

Mahogany Moon Publishing

Phoenix, Arizona

Dream Big!
@Author
Audrey

Ohhhh, I Can Be That With Esa!
Esa Bella that is!

Published by:
Mahogany Moon Publishing
Phoenix, Arizona
Phone: 623-877-9114
Email: ajohnsonmccurdy@yahoo.com

Audrey McCurdy, Publisher
QualityPress.info, Book Packager
Cover & Interior Illustrations by Henry Bosak

THIS BOOK BELONGS TO

DEDICATION

I dedicate this fun book to

my daughter

Serene D. McCurdy

Forever you are

My hummingbird

My inspiration

My LOVE

Keep holding my hand... and walk with me

Love Mommy

ACKNOWLEDGEMENTS

Thanks to my daughter, Serene, for taking this story I wrote in the 1980's and revising it to what it is now. Your celestial creativity & heart, your muse energies, your spirit keeps me hopeful. Thanks to my hubs, Dwight, for your support, and for your go get 'um vibe.

- Audrey

I would like to acknowledge my wife Tracy and my daughters Lindsey and Emily, they are there to inspire me and keep me grounded. Thank you for always believing in me.

- Henry

FOREWORD

I am honored to have been asked by my good friend Audrey McCurdy to write the Foreword to this book. I'm a lifelong reader and I especially enjoy books that inspire my imagination and creativity. This is Audrey's second book sharing the delightful adventures of her main character, Esa-Bella. *Ohhhh, I Can Be That with Esa!* explores the question children all over the world have been asked countless times, "What do you want to be when you grow up?" In her own whimsical way, Esa discovers the possibilities are endless. I discovered the answer to this question for myself in a great book as a child and all roads have lead me to a profession that has given me tremendous personal and professional satisfaction.

One of the greatest qualities we can cultivate in children is a sense of wonder. Reading offers a very accessible way for children to build upon their imagination and expand their understanding of the world around them. In this book, Esa takes us on her journey exploring the different hats we wear every day to find our purpose and place in the world.

What a wonderful way to inspire children to follow their dreams! It doesn't get any better than that! Happy reading!

Donna F. Williams, Esq.
Professional Mediator
http://www.donnathemediator.com

"Gotta go! I'm late for work!" gasped Esa~Bella's dad, as he kissed his family and hurried out the door. "Once again... I'm off to save the day!"

"Bye Daddy," Esa~Bella replied, as she munched on her pancakes.

"See you tonight honey," said Esa~Bella's mom. "Have a great day!"

3

"So mama?" Esa pondered. "Is daddy a Superhero?"

"A Superhero?" asked mama, wondering why Esa...Esa~Bella that is, would ask such a question.

"Sure, replied Esa. "Daddy just said he was 'off to save the day.' And, that's what Superheroes do. Right?"

Mama chuckled at the thought! "Yes and no Esa~Bella. Daddy's a psychologist, a doctor, who helps people think... happy thoughts."

Ohhhh, I get it. He's my daddy Dr. Benson," smiled Esa. "And mama...what about you? Are you a Superhero?"

"Well, sometimes I feel that way," Mama sighed, suddenly feeling weary. "I'm a woman who wears many hats…"

"Hats?" Esa interrupted.

"Sure!" Mama smirked. You see baby girl, I'm the nurse when you're sick. The taxi driver who takes you to dance lessons, tennis lessons, girl scouts, guitar…and um, the landscaper when our yard needs cutting…" Mama paused, heaving a hefty sigh. "But in real life I'm a College Professor…"

"You do a lot!" gasped Esa. "You are a Superhero!"

"That I am! I wear many hats… and one day you too will wear many hats! You can be that or this, or this and that…"

"Wearing a hat!?" Esa joyfully cried, as her eyes filled with wonder. "Yep, I can be that…
when I wear a hat."

Yes! I can be that when I wear a hat!

A top Chef, wearing my hat so tall!
So, come into my kitchen and let's have a ball.
Cutting and dicing.
Slicing it up!
Simmering and Seasoning
Pouring in an extra cup...
of edible eyeballs?

Ewwwwwww!
Yes, I can be that
when I wear a **Chef's Hat!**

Yes, I can be that when I wear a hat!

A cowboy!
Ooops, I mean a cowgirl
with my Stetson on.
Riding a mean, snorting bull
until the break of dawn.
Roughing and toughing
hanging on tight...with all my might!
Yeeee-Haw!
Yep, I can be that
when I wear a **Cowgirl Hat**.

11

Or I can be a Police Officer
proudly wearing my badge.
The enforcers,
here to protect and serve.
Me and my K9 buddy
catching the bad guys
and giving them what they deserve!

Yes, I can be that
when I wear a **Police Hat.**

Or I can be the leader of my Nation,
mindful of 'The Creation.'
Standing tall and proud,
Highlighting
my sacred **Headdress**
that I do avow.
A Native American Chief,
born of this land
echoing the voices
of my Ancestor's command.

Yes, I can be that
when I wear this majestic hat!

Ohhhh, I can be that!

"Oui, Oui."
A French Artist
wearing a **Beret!**
Painting masterpieces;
Flowery bouquets,
Hummingbirds' fantasies
and the Ocean blue.
Reddish, yellowish shades just for you.
Purple, Greenish paints
and more...
splashes of splatter.
Just colors, colors galore.

And
I can be a football player,
with my **Helmet** on.
Hut one, Hut two...HIKE! HIKE!
Running and blocking
as I hold onto the ball.
Running to score and feeling no pain!
Wheezing! Gasping!
Touchdown!
Touchdown!
We win the game!

Yes! I can be that
when I wear this kind of hat!

Or I can be an
English Guard
here to protect the adored Queen.
I stand frozen outside her Buckingham Palace.
Acting serious
but feeling ohhhh,
so serene.

Yes, I can be that
when I wear this **Bearskin Hat!**

Yes, I can be that when I wear a hat
A Firefighter!
That's what I'll be.
It's Hot, hot, hot!
Sizzle, fizzle, drizzle
feeling fiery.
Focusing
holding my heavy firehose
while seeing my brother
tangled and twisted
from his toes to his nose?

Yes, I can be that
when I wear a **Fireman's Hat!**

"Eeeesa! Esa~Bella," cried Momma, rousing her from her enchantment. "Where are you child? You need to finish breakfast... so we can go."

"Okay, mom" she sighed. I'm just sitting her...dreaming of being."

"Being a what?" Momma asked.

"Just thinking about what I want to be when I grow up."

Well good for you, but it's time to get ready for school. You need education first to get to be what you want to be. To get good grades, you have to study hard... be smart, learn a lot, ask questions and have fun!

 "Sure mom," sighed Esa~Bella, as she drifted back into her wonder.

Tap! Tap!
A Judge, that's what I'll be
donning my gigantic...**Big-Wig!**
Can you dig?
Banging my gavel
to get Donna the Meteor,
I mean Donna the Mediator's attention.
Order in the court, Judge Esa~Bella Benson
residing
Now everybody sit down,
before I send you all to detention!

Yes, I can be that
when I wear that kind of hat.

And I can be that when I wear this kind of hat.

A Mexican Mariachi singer
strumming my guitar
singing
¡Momma! Eres tan Hermosa para mi..."
On my head
a big straw **Sombrero** hat
and tapping my foot
patty...pat...pat.

Momma! You are so beautiful to me! **** ¡Momma! Eres tan Hermosa para me.

Or I can be this when I wear a Pirate's hat.

Searching for buried treasures
Out in the deep blue seas
Speaking in Buccaneer
Arrrrrr, Arrr, Arrrrrr!
Yep it's the Pirates life for me!

Yep, I can be that
when I wear a **Pirate's Hat.**

Spinning and whirling.
Tapping and prancing,
twirling and dancing.
I'm Light on my toes,
as the melody flows
dancing on air
just like the wonderful... Fred Astaire

Yes, I can be that
when I wear a **Top Hat!**

Or I can be that when I wear a **Hard Hat!**

A Construction worker
Building skyscrapers reaching for the sky
Saws,
hammers, nails
and other supplies...
Jackhammers, Oh my
that are really, really LOUD!
Floor by floor
we build
until we reach the
big fluffy clouds.

Esa! Eeeesa~Bella,' yelled Momma, "Stop that daydreaming, because it's time for school. We're going to be late!"

Okay, Mom," smirked Esa~Bella. "I really need school because boy, ohhhh boy, do I have a whole lot of learning to do!

WHAT DO YOU WANT TO BE
WHEN YOU GROW UP?

Your Name:_____   Date:_____

_____

_____

_____

_____

_____

_____

_____

_____

_____

_____

_____

_____

_____

ABOUT THE AUTHOR

AUDREY JOHNSONMCCURDY is a writer, a photographer and an artist. She worked for the Music/Entertainment Industry & photographed such greats as Michael Jackson, Bon Jovi, Aerosmith, M.C. Hammer & more... Her photographs have appeared in many Music Trade magazines, L.A. Times, Arizona newspapers and books of photography.

Audrey's published books are: a work of photographs titled "Visions of Santa Fe", a novel titled "SUBMERGED" & her first children's book "ZOO-SA-PALOOZA Time w/ Esa! Esa~Bella that is!" "Ohhhh, I Can Be That" is her fourth published book and the second children's book in the Esa~Bella series... with many more to come...

Born and raised in San Fernando, Ca, she now lives in Arizona.

ABOUT THE ILLUSTRATOR

Art has always been a big part of **HENRY BOSAK'S** life as far back as he can remember. The way he looks at it, he was always going to do something art related, there was no plan B.

As a graphic designer Henry has worked in the print industry for years. His graphic designs are mostly done digitally but his real love is to work with pencil and paper or paint and brush. His graphics have been seen all across the county and Canada and if you have gotten a mail piece from a radio station, at some point, then you probably have seen his work. "Ohhhh, I Can Be That" is his first children's book!

Painting is something that Henry has always enjoyed doing and recently he has dedicated himself (and quite a few canvases) to strengthen his painting skills. Henry is represented in two galleries in Arizona and hopes to keep painting and doing art for as long as he can pick up a pencil or brush.

CPSIA information can be obtained at www.ICGtesting.com
Printed in the USA
LVIW01n0543021116
510773LV00002B/2